A FOX STORY

A Fox Story

by Allan Sollers

with illustrations by William Reusswig

 A Young Owl Book Holt, Rinehart and Winston, Inc., New York

Copyright © 1963 by Holt, Rinehart and Winston, Inc.
Library of Congress Catalog Card Number 63-9582
Printed in the United States of America
All rights reserved
4-9771-0313
66E5

This is a true story. It began one noontime when I was a boy in a country school in Calvert County, Maryland. The day was sunny and cool, just right for a ball game or a chase through the woods.

We rushed noisily out of the school door when Miss Elaine dismissed us—the big boys first, followed by the girls and smaller children. There were sixteen of us in school, ranging from first to eighth graders.

Suddenly, Charles stopped and held up his hands for silence. Because he was the strongest and smartest boy in school, the rest of us immediately obeyed. He said nothing, but his expression told us to be patient.

He cocked his head to one side, listening. Then he asked, "Do you hear that? Them's hounds!"

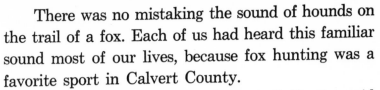

There was no mistaking the sound of hounds on the trail of a fox. Each of us had heard this familiar sound most of our lives, because fox hunting was a favorite sport in Calvert County.

"I'll bet they're coming this way," Charles said breathlessly.

"The last time they chased that fox, he crossed through the cornfield and ran right down to Rawlings Cove," I said. Capt'n Jim, who never missed a hunt if he could help it, had told me about the last one when the fox had outsmarted the hounds along the north shore of the cove.

"Let's go!" Henry shouted. "Maybe the fox is headed for the cove again!"

"It sounds like it!" exclaimed Charles.

Charles took off across the schoolyard with Henry close behind him. The rest of us upper-grade boys followed, each carrying his lunch sack.

"What about us?" the girls shouted.

"We'll tell you all about it when we get back!" Charles answered.

It was an unwritten law that the girls and the smaller boys never followed us when we took to the woods during the noon hour. This was one of the privileges that we older boys enjoyed, the right to have some time to ourselves.

Charles and Henry led the way through the woods to the fence that bordered the lower end of the cornfield. When we arrived at the fence, the pack of hounds was much closer.

"The fox is coming this way for sure," Tom whispered.

"If Capt'n Jim finds us here, he'll skin us alive," I said. "He has no use for kids on a fox hunt."

Charles had the same idea. We were uninvited guests, and this was no time to meet the hunters face to face. He turned quickly to climb a huge pine tree that grew near the fence. The rest of us followed up the stair-step limbs and climbed quickly to the tree-top. There we settled down in our majestic grandstand to wait for whatever might happen.

We opened our sacks to eat our lunches, but we were careful not to make any noise. The hounds were still some distance away, although we now could tell that the fox was leading them to Rawlings Cove.

Then, heavenly days! A full-grown red fox trotted out of the bushes just to the left of us and stopped at the edge of the field, looking in the direction of the hounds. The fox was not more than fifty yards away. All of us saw him at the same moment.

Fortunately, the wind was in our favor. The fox obviously had not caught our scent. He stood calmly, unalarmed by the approach of the dogs.

His actions were puzzling. It looked as if he were waiting for the hounds instead of running from them. His unruffled coat and his brisk step showed no signs of weariness. I knew that we were seeing a fox use all of his cunning to avoid the dogs, but just what he was up to baffled me.

A moment later we were even more confused. A second fox appeared at the edge of the cornfield. This fox was much smaller than the first, and was apparently the vixen mate of the first fox. She was wet, muddy, and obviously weary. There was no doubt that this second fox was the one the hounds were trailing.

Coming along the edge of the cornfield, the vixen ran directly to her mate. She brushed against him, and then ran to a gap in the fence that surrounded the field. She leaped to the top rail of the log fence and, like a tightrope walker, moved quickly along until she vanished from sight.

In spite of the fact that the pack of dogs was coming quite close, the male fox showed no alarm. With calm deliberateness, he flattened down on his stomach and began crawling on the grass. He continued moving in this fashion toward the fence where his mate had leaped from the ground to the top rail. After he had passed five or six feet beyond this point, he leaped to his feet and flashed away toward the cove.

All of us had heard that foxes would relieve each other when they were being chased by hounds. Here we had seen it happen! The male fox had come to the rescue of his mate and was deliberately leading the dogs in another direction! We were greatly impressed by the way in which the fox had made sure that the hounds would follow him instead of his tired mate.

Suddenly, the pack of hounds burst out of the woods with frenzied baying. They followed the scent of the fox along the edge of the cornfield and to the gap in the fence. In a few moments, they had passed beneath us and were off chasing the male fox to the cove. Not one of them caught the scent of the vixen that had escaped them by running along the top of the rail fence.

The hunters arrived quickly, following the dogs. They passed below us without knowing that we had viewed them from our treetop seats.

When we were certain that they were gone, we scrambled down the tree in wild amazement. We ran to the fence and viewed at close range the rails along which the vixen had traveled.

"Wasn't that something?" Henry said in breathless admiration.

"Wait 'til the kids hear about this!" said Charles.

A clanging schoolbell summoned us back through the woods which stood between the cornfield and the schoolyard. The excitement with which we told the story of seeing the fox hunt caused everyone to gather around us. Miss Elaine encouraged us to tell in detail what we had seen. For more than a half hour we recounted each of the details. Then Miss Elaine reminded us that we should get on with our studies. It was hard to settle down to reading and arithmetic with the memory of the foxes so fresh in our minds.

The next day after school, Charles signaled to us. We knew by his actions that a secret communication was to be delivered, so we followed him to the edge of the schoolyard.

"I heard the men talking down at the store last night," Charles began. "They are going fox hunting again on Saturday."

"Capt'n Jim said that the fox outsmarted him yesterday," I added. "He's bound to catch that fox if it's the last thing he ever does."

"The men plan to bring in another pack of hounds," Charles said.

"Well, what about it?" asked Henry. "Is there any chance that they'll take us along?"

"No, they'll never change their minds about us," Charles answered. "The best that we can hope for is another look at the fox like yesterday. Let's plan to

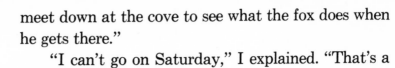

meet down at the cove to see what the fox does when he gets there."

"I can't go on Saturday," I explained. "That's a work day. My mom has a lot of things laid out for me to do."

"Getting away on Saturday will be hard for all of us," Charles agreed. "But tell your mothers that I've invited you up to my house Saturday. Beg hard! We don't want to miss seeing the foxes again."

"Oh, we'll be there, all right," said Henry. "Saturday work or no, we'll be there."

"We'll all meet at my house and go to the south shore of Rawlings Cove," Charles added. "We can sit in them big trees down there and see what happens."

"Everybody better bring along something to eat," said Henry. "We won't be getting much lunch, more than likely."

When our plans to view the fox hunt on Saturday were completed, our group meeting broke up and we started toward home.

On Saturday, six of us who had gained our mothers' consent gathered at Charles's house at the appointed hour. We waited thirty minutes longer to make sure that no one would be left behind. Then we headed for the cove. Henry looked at his watch. It was almost eleven o'clock. Most of us knew the time anyway, by the empty feeling in our stomachs and by the position of the sun in the sky.

"We'll catch thunder if Capt'n Jim finds us spying on him," I said.

"He won't find us," Charles said. "We'll be careful."

"He'll blister us good if we interfere with the hunt, but it will be worth it to see the foxes again," Henry said with a nervous laugh.

We moved quietly to the cove and climbed up a big tree on the south side of the water. We agreed that no one would call out or say anything—no matter what happened. Each of us had brought a couple of apples which we slipped out of our pockets and began eating as silently as we could.

Our timing was excellent! Shortly after we were settled in the treetop, we heard the hounds trailing the fox. Their baying steadily became louder. Charles gave a signal for all of us to remain perfectly still, and pointed to the opposite side of the cove where the fox might first appear.

Our tension mounted as we watched intently for the first sign of the fox. The baying of the hounds indicated that he was coming closer all the time.

Suddenly, the fox broke from the bushes at a dead run! He crossed the clearing between the bushes and the shore in a flash. When he reached the edge of the water, he made a tremendous leap into the creek. It looked to me as if the fox had jumped at least twenty feet! Charles said later that he was sure the leap had been longer than that.

In any event, when the fox hit the water, he began to swim up the cove and out from the shore. We thought he was swimming around a fallen, giant pine tree whose thick, downward limbs held the trunk a few feet above the water. The fox, however, had a different idea.

When he reached the outer end of the tree, he turned and swam in among its branches. He moved in close under the tree trunk, then disappeared from sight. Obviously, he had flattened himself against one of the big limbs, with only the tip of his nose above the water. In this position, he would be most difficult for the hounds to find.

Soon the hunters and the hounds arrived. There was a great commotion. The hounds broke into the clearing, and eagerly sniffed the scent of the fox up to the water's edge. Then they lost it. Both dogs and men moved up and down the shore, seeking the track or scent of the fox. But not a trace of their quarry did they find.

Then Capt'n Jim's most dependable hound, Old Belle, jumped upon the trunk of the fallen tree and began to follow it out from the shore.

"Oh, go back, old hound, go back!" was my silent prayer. I was sure that my companions felt the same as I did.

The hound was now halfway out to the end of the tree trunk! My blood pounded in my veins as I contemplated the fate of the fox. Was the fox holding his breath as I was? Could Old Belle see the fox submerged in the water? Could she possibly smell the fox's breath at that distance? Would the hound work her way out to the end of the tree trunk, or would the protruding limbs stop her?

As if in answer to our prayers, the hound stopped. She slowly turned around and started back toward the shore.

Momentarily, the fox seemed safe. Then a hunter asked, "Do you suppose the fox is out on that old tree?"

"No," replied Capt'n Jim. "That was my best hound. Old Belle would have spotted that fox if he was in the vicinity of that tree. I think that fox swam the creek. I'll take my hounds around the head of the cove and down the other shore. You fellows follow this shoreline down, and one of us should find the spot where the fox left the water to go back in the woods."

Once again I prayed, "Oh, Fox, don't move too soon!"

Capt'n Jim and his hounds were coming around the head of the cove. They were going to pass the tree in which we were hidden. We breathed deeply and prepared for the moment of the passing. Even if they found us now, I wouldn't care. The fox was safe. What would we say if they found us? My fears were unnecessary, for Capt'n Jim and his hounds passed below us without a moment's hesitation.

When each party had examined the shoreline without finding a trace of the fox, they made new plans.

"That scamp got away again," Capt'n Jim called to his friends. "I think he followed the swamp up toward Murray's farm. Take the road on your side and meet me at the schoolhouse."

Then they were gone. Minutes passed before the fox moved. Finally, we noticed a slight ripple in the water where the fox had hidden. He raised his head above the surface. He made no sound. When he was sure that he was safe, he swam back down the cove to the spot where he had entered the water. He crawled up on a flat rock that lay quite close to the shore, and shook the water from his fur. After looking cautiously about, he leaped from the rock to the grass and was gone.

Then Charles gave the signal to break silence. We all started chattering at once. We climbed down the tree, elated by the fox's cunning.

"That's the smartest fox I ever knew," said Henry.

"And we won't ever tell his secret," said Charles. "Let's all pledge that we won't tell his hiding place."

As far as I know, not one of us boys ever broke the pledge in the fox's lifetime.